THE MINISTRY— CAREER OR CALLING?

OR

WHERE IN THE BIBLE DO YOU FIND "SENIOR PASTOR"?

Gordon K. Reed

Cover art by Hannah

Printed in the United States of America

ISBN: 1-884416-56-X

CONTENTS

This book is dedicated with affection and appreciation to many of my former students at Reformed Theological Seminary and especially to Earl Adams, Dan King, Bill Lyle, Tom Shoger, Charlie Stakely, and Patrick Womack who are so obviously called of the Lord to be Preachers of the Word, and Shepherds to the flock of God.

INTRODUCTION

When did it begin? Where did it come from? (maybe C. S. Lewis' "Wormwood" is for real?) It's probably been there all along just waiting for the right conditions to emerge in epidemic form. The epidemic is upon us, but few seem to realize that the disease is deadly and may kill multiplied millions before it is brought under control.

The "it" to which I refer is a subtle but definite change in the ministry of the church and in the attitude and expectations of those who choose the ministry as their career. For most who follow this pathway, there is an initial, strong sense of calling from the Lord. This may mean giving up a promising career in business or one of the professions. It may also involve selling a comfortable house, uprooting the family, and settling into a crowded apartment in order to attend seminary and gain the required credentials for the ministry.

Quite often much of the idealism is lost during those trying and testing years of seminary. An academic setting is a difficult one in which to maintain a fervency of spirit, and a close walk with the Lord. In fact, when I was teaching in seminary I observed that some students rarely attended church, unless they were asked to preach which was seldom. Precious and saving truths are analyzed, scrutinized, and dissected. The everyday grind of enormous amounts of reading, writing, and constant study tends to diminish the time spent in loving devotion and soul-refreshing prayer. The professors of which the student has heard all his life, and whom he has idealized in his mind as super saints, turn out to be mere human beings—fallen, fractious, and maybe even a little vain and distant.

The guest speakers who address the students in chapel services are seldom the hard working and hard-fighting yeomen from the trenches of spiritual battle, but only those who are models of success (success being defined in terms of the size of church, budget, and contributions to the seminary). While it is true that these speakers may be faithful servants of Christ, all too often they are extolled and held up as the only acceptable role models for aspiring young pastors. And unless they are very careful, such spiritual giants may begin to believe the flattering introduction heaped upon them by the president of the seminary who remains very much aware of their clout and potential for even larger contributions.

Often one senses an air of self-importance, quite different from the spirit the Lord Jesus talked about when he was in the upper room with His disciples. As a result of this and other contributing factors they (the guest speakers) may have become carriers of this deadly virus of pride which the seminarian may contract by the most casual exposure, such as sitting in Chapel while they speak.

Most seminaries offer courses in leadership, as they should; but all too often the idea of "CEO" is transferred to the ministry, and in the process "CEO" becomes "Senior Pastor." The students are exhorted to go after the "movers and shakers" in the community, and are assured that if they do, these redeemed elite will in turn reach out to the masses; a sort of trickle-down spirituality. Of course, there is no biblical proof offered that such a concept comes from the Lord, or even pleases Him, but the proof is in the corporate world, and as the student is often reminded, "all truth is God's truth."

So the day for graduation finally comes. Equipped with all the skills in languages, biblical studies, systematic theology, not to mention all the latest techniques for success, the student stands on the threshold of a whole new chapter in his life, imbued with a burning desire for success in the Lord's work, driven by the holy ambition to make his school proud of him, and so be invited back one day to address a future generation of aspiring young pastors.

Thus, the well-equipped young pastor-to-be is ready to launch out into a rewarding career, in which his potential will be recognized and developed. He may even accept the fact that for the first few years he may have to pastor a small- to medium-sized congregation, or be an "associate" (heaven forbid, not an "assistant") for a short time, but then he will climb the ladder of success, making sure along the way that he associates with the "right people" in the denomination. He reasonably expects a fulfilling life that offers both satisfaction and a fairly good living as well, little knowing or even suspecting what awaits him out there. Of which things we will speak as this book develops, unless I have been drawn and quartered before then—which is a distinct possibility.

CHAPTER 1
OUT OF THE FRYING PAN . . . MAYBE

This is a case study (of sorts) of one particular student who is late in his senior year of seminary, and anxious to join the ranks of the rising young stars of the denomination, knowing he has all the tools necessary to make his mark in the heady ecclesiastical world. In his mind he can almost hear the holy chant of "ready, set, go!"

So our young seminarian comes to the end of his seminary training. He will be back in three years or so because everyone says, "you'll never really advance in your career without a Doctor of Ministry." (known by the "in" crowd as D. Min.) He is sure that his grasp of theology is well above average, he is confident that he really knows the original languages. Why he may even have his morning devotions in Hebrew, or at least he tells folks that he does. He understands the panoramic scope of church History. The few so-called practical courses in ministry seemed boring, undignified, and irrelevant, especially when the "real" studies seemed so exciting and important.

His game plan is simple. He will begin as associate pastor in a fairly large church. If the senior pastor who comes to interview him suggests a position as assistant, he will point out to the poor fellow that "assistant" is neither dignified nor biblical, and that he will consider only an associate position. He may have heard rumors that the older pastor is slipping a bit, and a lot of the younger leadership is chaffing under his outmoded style of ministry. Maybe if he handles himself well, who knows what might develop in that sort of situation? Not that he would do anything to undermine the people's confidence in their pastor, but at the same time he would certainly have to be available if there was a slippage on the part of the senior pastor.

Plan B is almost as acceptable as the above. It, too, is fairly simple. He will consider a call to a midsize church as "senior" pastor, if it is located in a growing town, and the leadership in that church is visionary and open to new ideas about growing and marketing the church, and if they will be reasonable about the cost of living these days. About three to five years in such a situation should prepare him for a significant step up. During those years, he will of course want to work on his D. Min. degree, and after all, a man in his mid-thirties with a "Doctorate" has to be on his way up. Perhaps at this point the reader needs to be educated about that all important degree. The D. Min degree was developed for a number of reasons, few if any of which will ever be broadcast to the people in the pews. This degree requires a little less than the average Master's degree in most educational institutions, but somehow "Doctor" sounds so much more impressive than Master. Its appeal is twofold. 1.) It is a remarkable money maker for the seminaries offering the degree. 2.) It appeals to the ego and a sense of pride in the student, which virtues are not at all rare in the ministry. Of course some of the courses are even helpful in the ministry, but who would offer them if there was not a considerable financial reward for the school, and who would take them unless one could obtain the much coveted D. Min? (Now I've done it! I'll never be invited to speak in a seminary ever again!)

Let's return to the story of our aspiring and about-to-graduate seminarian. He inwardly shudders as he hears horror stories about former graduates who are stuck in small towns with nothing but maintenance ministry. The somewhat disturbing statistics about how many ordained ministers out there are without churches, and how many seminary graduates are being cranked out every year with the same kind of preparation he has received must be ignored, or at least he must understand that there is always room at the top for truly gifted men.

Come March 1 of his senior year he is more than a little annoyed that the dumb people who work in the placement office still have not given him opportunity for the kind of interviews which match his exceptional skills, but after all they have their pets, mostly clods who have no apparent ambition, so what can one expect? Undaunted, he makes 117 copies of his very impressive résumé and begins to send them out to the "right" churches, and to a number of the "movers and shakers" in the denomination who will see to it that he has the right connections.

Soon we will see what happens and how our hero responds when a touch of reality begins to penetrate this veil of self-importance.

CHAPTER 2
INTO THE FIRE — FOR SURE

The aspiring young pastor-to-be anxiously awaits his first call. Each day seems like a month as graduation draws near, and no offer is forthcoming. The mail is unreliable, he assures himself, and there have been gaps when no one has manned the phones in the apartment. Perhaps these things alone can explain the lack of response from the many resumes he has sent out. He talks with other students who are having the same problem; no help there. There are students who have already been placed, or have received calls on their own. The really surprising, and even disappointing, thing about all this is that those who smugly talk about their positions are nowhere nearly as gifted as he is sure he is. There's no explaining pulpit committees, and "senior pastors" who are looking for prospective associates.

An appointment with the president is very business like and short, not at all like it was when the selfsame president was speaking in the home church a few years ago, and eagerly recruiting our hero. Then he seemed so genuinely interested and even friendly, but now somewhat remote and maybe a bit annoyed that his valuable time is being taken by such an inconsequential matter. So the young man is sent to the placement officer. Somewhat discouraged that the President seems so disinterested, he expects little if any help; still there is always a possibility that placement may have something to offer commensurate with the obviously over looked gifts which need an opportunity to develop and impress.

Much to his surprise the placement officer, who is also dean of students, clerk of faculty, chaplain in the U. S. Marines

(Reserves), and supply pastor of a small church in another town, greets him with the good news that two openings have just been brought to his attention.

The first one is a youth pastor position in a large affluent congregation. Yes, they have had six youth pastors in the last four years, but a real opportunity for ministry is offered, and they have a nice basement apartment in the home of the widow of the former clerk of session, who needs only an occasional look-in by the youth pastor's wife in exchange for a very reasonable rental rate. The nice thing about it is that he will be expected to mow the lawn (all two acres) no more than once a week, except during the spring and summer months of course.

After politely suggesting that this may be one of the few areas in which he is not gifted, the now shaken student is almost afraid to ask about number two. However, the magic words, "senior pastor" position brings new life and hope. Yes, there is a senior pastor position opening, and they may even be willing to consider an exceptionally mature and gifted seminarian. Then the other shoe falls. The church is located in a town of 782 people, approximately 65 miles from the nearest "large city" of 15,000. How large is the church? 27 communing members and 2 children. Average age? 74. There are 11 male members; six of whom are elders, and five are deacons. The pay is "average" and will be discussed only with a man who is ready to accept a call.

At this point he asks for time to pray and consider. As he makes his way dejectedly home he is appalled to think what his peers would say (not to mention his wife who had never planned to marry a preacher anyway) if they knew he was considering such a call. Surely better opportunities will come his way before graduation, but alas, none are forthcoming.

Since two of the six youth pastors in the first mentioned opening have since been committed to the mentally ill wing of the state hospital, and since he doesn't even own a lawn mower, the youth position possibility in the large city church is eliminated. With much encouragement from the placement officer and the President who confidentially tells him "there is some real money in that little church, and they do have a fairly nice, if somewhat quaint, manse," our hero agrees to a trial sermon. So early Sunday morning, he and his wife travel five hours through what appears to be mostly barren wilderness to the little village of Eureka. (Don't forget the derivation of that word!) There is no difficulty finding the church, it is one of three churches right around the town square. The small church with the impressive name of FIRST PRESBYTERIAN, ESTABLISHED 1852 is almost half filled for the service. The sermon goes well, with two poems, a reference or so to the "original languages", and three well ordered, if somewhat boring, points. After the service one of the Elders, who identifies himself as "Clerk of Session" congratulates him on a fine sermon, then asks; "when can you move? No, a congregational meeting will not be necessary, I pretty much run this church. No one would stay for a meeting anyway, have to beat those pesky Baptist to the one and only cafe in town." And just like that he becomes senior pastor of First Presbyterian church. He will discover he is also secretary, janitor, handyman, and yard keeper, and a host of others things too. The Salary will be discussed after he arrives in town. All moving expenses will be paid, providing he rents a U-Haul trailer.

Now what? A whole lot more and less than the young pastor ever suspects.

CHAPTER 3
OUCH! THE FIRE IS HOT!

The stirring and challenging graduation ceremonies and speeches are at an end, and at least some of the excitement virtually lost along the way in the seminary years is recovered. Moving day is at hand. Good-byes are said. Fellow students help with the loading of the rented trailer, and our ex-seminarian, soon to be "Reverend" (once Presbytery exams are over) and family are off to the first step in a career (or is it a calling?) which hopefully will take them to where they have dreamed of being for many a long year.

When they arrive in Eureka, they discover that the women's organization has prepared them a nice hot meal, and food in the pantry for a week or more. Things are looking up. Then down again, because the plumbing isn't working very well, and the deacon in charge of house and grounds and manse forgot to check on the air-conditioner, which doesn't work and will take a week or more to repair. But, all in all, the move has gone well, and the people have gone out of their way to make him feel at home. So far, so good. His disdain of small churches in small towns has softened, just a little bit.

The church treasurer comes by with a check to reimburse him for the moving expenses, and a half month's salary in advance. Maybe this won't be too bad after all. Then the other shoe falls. A call comes from the Chairman of Presbytery's committee on credentials who demands to know why he has moved on the field before he has been examined and approved by Presbytery? As much as it pains him to plead ignorance about anything, he must confess he didn't really know he was not supposed to, and besides he really had no

19

other place to take his family. After all, he had been told to leave his seminary apartment by the first Monday after graduation. The chairman informs him that neither excuse is really acceptable, and that he must come to a called meeting of the committee to deal with his situation. The chairman also reminds him of the terrible inconvenience of a called meeting, as well as the added expense of travel for the committee members.

Trembling with fear at his first encounter with the awesome and omnipotent power of COMMITTEE, he sets out the next day with heart and hat in hand to ask for leniency and consideration of his plight. He comforts himself with the thought that these men are all Christian brothers who will be more understanding than the haughty chairman. (Oh, yeah?)

The encounter is grueling, humiliating, and humbling. After seven hours of intense questioning, he is informed that he knows very little theology (he actually forgot *Ordo Salutis*), practically no English Bible, and absolutely no Polity. "What do they teach in seminary these days anyhow?" is muttered over and over again by these understanding Christian brothers.

In spite of it all, he is given grudging permission to stay in the manse at First Church until Presbytery meets, but under no circumstances is he to preach more than twice a month until he is officially ordained, which may or may not happen after his examination before the Presbytery. Bewildered and inwardly seething at the unreasonableness of the COMMITTEE, he nevertheless returns home to cram for yet another exam and to explain to his new church why he can't preach on a regular basis for the next seven weeks.

This brings him to the first meeting of the officers of the church. He only vaguely remembers that there was something in his polity course about Session meetings, but he can't find his notes for that class, and then remembers he sat on the back row that day, and studied his Greek declensions, which at the moment don't seem quite as important as they did back at seminary.

As soon as he returns, a call is placed to the clerk of Session asking for a called meeting of the Elders right after church on Sunday. "You surely don't mean before Sunday dinner do you son? Why, not only the Baptist, but the Methodist, and Pentecostals would all get to the café before us, and we can't have that now can we? Sure after church Sunday evening would be fine, except none of the Elders come to church at night any more. Maybe you can get them there if you call. Oh no, son, I can't call them, that's what we pay you for, ha ha." This is an expression our pastor is doomed to hear about almost every chore under the sun, minus the "ha, ha" most of the time. So after much persuasion, three of the six Elders agree to meet, and of this meeting we will no doubt learn in the next chapter.

CHAPTER 4
EDITORIAL AND HISTORICAL
INTERLUDE — REALLY HOT!

The few people who have read this have asked if I have any person or any church in particular in mind. So far as it refers to a seminary student, later pastor, or to a specific congregation, the answer is, *of course not!* The face of the young man in question is sort of like the composite drawing on the local post office bulletin board; it reminds you vaguely of almost everyone you've ever seen. In fact, any resemblance to anyone living or dead is strictly coincidental and most assuredly unintentional; well, almost anyway. I'll let you figure out any exceptions.

Before getting back to our young pastor's first Session meeting, and his subsequent conviction that the Lord must have something else in mind for him, a broader field in which his talents might be put to use, I must relate a conversation that took place in my office at seminary several years ago. One of the staff personnel, a lovely Christian lady who worked diligently for the Lord, both at the seminary, where she was rewarded with an absurdly low salary, but the honor of "working for the Kingdom," and in her local church, asked for an appointment. When she came to my office she was obviously distressed, and even a little depressed. After a few moments of pleasant exchanges, she asked, with tears welling up in her eyes, "Pastor, does God always call ministers to larger churches and more pay?" "Why do you ask?" I replied. "Well, we've just lost our fifth pastor in the last eight years. He told us the Lord was calling him to another church, and like the four others before him, the church to which he is going is larger than our congregation and is able to pay him more money." "No my dear, I don't think God always calls men to larger churches which pay better salaries, but I do think many of us are unduly influenced by these considerations." The conversation still haunts me, and in some ways provided the impetus for this book. What a question! It raises another. Is the ministry a career or calling, or where in all the Bible do you find "senior pastor"?

Now back to the story. Our young pastor friend is facing his first session meeting at which he must tell the elders that the Presbytery's COMMITTEE has informed him that his move on the field was improper, and that he will not be allowed to preach on a regular basis until after he passes his Presbytery's examination for ordination, which is not a foregone conclusion. (No use upsetting the Elders with that little bombshell.) After a somewhat shortened Sunday evening service, at which only one of the Elders is present, the pastor makes his way to his study, wondering if the other two who promised to attend will show up. Within a few minutes the three of six Elders who promised to come are present, and the meeting begins.

When the problem is presented, the elders make two very sensible motions. 1.) That the retired Baptist preacher who lives in a nearby town, and is first cousin of the church Pianist, be invited to fill the pulpit on the Sundays our pastor is not allowed to preach, with the understanding that no Baptism will take place until after the pastor's ordination. "Not too bad, maybe I have underestimated the wisdom of these godly men," thinks the pastor to himself. 2.) That the Baptist pastor be paid half the pastor's salary during this time. Both motions pass unanimously. The shock is profound, but he manages not to weep openly, and, come to think of it, they still haven't told him what his salary is to be. This is not the best time to broach that subject.

Upon his crestfallen return to the manse, our young pastor confides to his wife that he believes the Lord may be calling him to another field very soon. His poor wife is still struggling to adjust to a small Deep South town, far from any city, and even further from her family and friends. "Why don't we just pack up and leave right now?" she sobs. "But, honey," he pleads, "we can't do that. Where would we go, and how could I support you? Please be patient and I'll have you out of this dump before long." With these and many other comforting words, he manages to calm her down, and somewhere between midnight and dawn they both drift off into a troubled sleep. How he goes about seeking another call will be revealed in later chapters.

CHAPTER 5
A LIGHT IN THE DARKNESS — MAYBE

The weeks pass quickly during which our young pastor is forced to live with the awkward situation of being unable to preach in his church on a regular basis until he passes his Presbytery exams and is ordained. A far more awkward situation is attempting to live on just one half of a very meager salary. His first paycheck is a profound shock! It is far less than half of what he thought he would be receiving. A distress call goes out to the church treasurer, who is very hard of hearing, especially on the phone. "I think there has been a little misunderstanding about my paycheck," he laments, and quickly learns that the treasurer is extremely sensitive to any implied criticism. "But the Elders told me my salary was more than what is indicated on this check, even allowing for half pay."

"Did they also tell you that your medical insurance, your automobile expense, your retirement, and social security all had to come out of your salary?" Welcome to the world of church finances, young man! He remembers with some nostalgia and a tinge of bitterness that in his former career, the company never took all these deductions from his salary!

The Sundays he preaches he is made very much aware that most of the congregation prefers the Sundays when the retired Baptist minister preaches. He also feels a growing conviction that the Lord will have something better for him soon, so he buckles down to study, even to visit some of the congregation, and prepare for his examination before Presbytery. It could just be that the Lord is teaching him a little humility; a most desirable but exceedingly rare virtue in the ministry.

It is at this point he remembers the sage advice given in a chapel address by the seminary president. "Young men, if you ever expect to 'get anywhere in the ministry' you must get to know the prominent pastors in the denomination, and benefit from their wisdom and influence." Ah, now he knows what to do. The first step is to write to several of these men in appropriately humble and adoring language, and request to be put on their mailing list for tapes, church bulletins, and newsletters. He also requests two of these pastors who live within a reasonable distance to serve on his Ordination commission. He thinks better of adding, "if I pass my exams."

Much to his delight one of them accepts the invitation and two more write notes, condescending to put him on their mailing list for tapes. All three of these men become aware that a bright young man is taking his place in the denomination.

The Presbytery exam actually goes better than he ever imagined it could, and the date is set for his Ordination. It escapes his notice that the Presbytery docket is extremely full and that many of the members are on coffee break during his examination. It is noted with some surprise by members of the Presbytery that the Reverend Doctor Goodbody has agreed to preach the ordination sermon.

The service of Ordination is somber, impressive, and thrilling. When he takes the vows of ordination and installation, a holy awe comes over him that is both humbling and at the same time exhilarating. It is far more than just a ritual. He senses that something real has happened in his heart that will remain with him for the rest of his life.

After the service and following reception, the crowd thins, but Dr. Goodbody remains for a brief chat. "Work hard, my young friend, do a good job, and when you feel your task here is completed, let me know, I may be able to help you." His euphoric joy is scarcely diminished by the next words; "Will your deacons be sending me a check for my travel expenses, or should I wait for it now?" (Why hadn't he thought of that?)

"I will have it in the mail to you first thing, you know how forgetful these deacons can be!" He thanks Dr. Goodbody for the most impressive sermon he has ever heard, apologizes again for the failure to have a check ready, and sends the stately Reverend Goodbody on his way. Then and only then, our hero collapses in relief. At long last he is on his way; senior pastor of First Presbyterian Church, and at least known by name by some real "shakers and movers." Sure the town and church are small, but it is FIRST PRESBYTERIAN CHURCH, and He is SENIOR PASTOR.

The weeks become months, and the months become a year. The congregation, though not exactly ecstatic with his ministry, seems reasonably content, and a few show signs of true and sincere affection. In spite of himself the pastor begins to feel a growing bond, and a love for his people. The problems are many. He is expected to do almost everything, and the neat, well ordered schedule he had laid out for himself never seems to work out. He and his wife struggle to live on the small salary. Still there is a growing restlessness, and he discovers a new phrase from one of the journals he takes and even occasionally reads. The word is "maintenance ministry." He also learns this is not a good phrase.

It refers to situations much like his own, where there is little growth, and many demands on him for pastoral care. His congregation is aging, and the insecurities of old age have created many fears, anxieties, and real problems. Long pastoral visits, which are never frequent enough nor long enough to satisfy his parishioners, take up much of his time and energy. The fascinating and enlightening studies he laboriously prepares are received with little enthusiasm by his parishioners who seem unable to appreciate the details of the nuances of Greek and Hebrew, and so far as he knows have never even heard of Turretin's *Institutes of Elenctic Theology*, or even Butler's *Analogy*. When he argues long and passionately in behalf of presuppositional apologetics, he is greeted with blank looks and scarcely stifled yawns. He longs for a more theologically sophisticated congregation. His restlessness grows, never thinking that hard work and more attention to the personal relationships in the congregation might be a better cure than a move. But his career seems so stymied in Eureka.

CHAPTER 6
DISCOVERING HOW IMPORTANT IT IS
TO KNOW REALLY IMPORTANT PASTORS

As the days, weeks and months dragged slowly by, there was no change in the depressing situation, and no one seemed at all interested in seeing anything happen in the church. The worship services were dull and uninspiring, the music atrocious, (they sang "In the Garden" and "Love Lifted Me" almost every Sunday), the offerings barely able to meet expenses, and the attendance was disappointing. Very few people of any age came to Sunday School, and often the teachers just didn't bother to show up. For the morning worship service, the sanctuary was less than half full, and no more than ten or twelve people attended the evening service. Five or six people came to prayer meeting, but no one but old Mrs. Smythe would pray aloud, and often no one at all showed up for that service.

When the pastor suggested that they try something different on Sunday and Wednesday evening, the Session voted his ideas down and reprimanded him for even suggesting such a thing. Of course only one or two of the Elders ever came to these services, but they still insisted that the services continue, and no, they were not at all interested in small groups or home Bible studies, and seemed to think these things were just gimmicks of the liberals to take over the church.

Then a sudden bright shaft of light penetrated this darkness when one day the young pastor read in the newsletter from one of the larger churches in a city not too far away, a glowing account of the great blessing enjoyed by that congregation when the renowned Reverend Doctor, Eim N. Portant conducted a series of services in that congregation. The notice read something like this: "What an experience we enjoyed this past week. Dr. Portant preached powerfully and brilliantly. We were thrilled to hear him once again, and the afterglow of his gracious presence will linger for a long time in our hearts. He is such a dynamic speaker and we rejoiced to hear of his wonderful ministry in his own church, which by his own words is one of the most significant churches in our whole denomination."

It was almost like a revelation from heaven! "That's what we need here," he thought. "I wonder if the Session would possibly agree to an invitation to Dr. Portant to hold a conference in our church?" His wife thought it was a great idea and reminded him that "it had been years since she had a new outfit." "If such a great man would come to preach for us, I would just die if he saw me in any of my old and drab dresses or suits." "Honey," he replied, "if we can get Dr. Portant to come, I'll buy you a whole new outfit, even if we have to borrow the money." (Which of course they would.)

When the idea was presented to the Session, he was surprised by their enthusiastic response. "But how would a little church like ours ever be able to get such a 'big time' preacher?," they asked. Our hero did not actually say it, but certainly implied that he and ol' Eim were long time friends, and he was sure Dr. Portant would be delighted to come. After all such a man wasn't in the ministry for money and fame! (Oh the innocence of youth!) Then a motion was made that the pastor invite Dr. Portant to hold a series of services in the church at his earliest convenience. The motion was quickly seconded, but before a vote could be take, the motion was amended to include "a fee will be paid up to but not more than $250 for these services." That amendment was also quickly seconded.

The pastor pled with the Elders not to adopt the amendment, as this small amount would surely insult the famous Doctor. "Well pastor", replied one of the elders, "since Dr. Portant isn't in the ministry for fame or riches, what difference would it make?" "I would like to amend the amendment" said another elder, "To the effect that if the 'love offering' exceeds $250, we pass that along to Dr. Portant, provided the over and above would not be more than $100."

Another elder made the very wise suggestion that no amount be mentioned to Dr. Portant, only that a very generous honorarium would be forthcoming. "Let's surprise him" were his words.

"Oh, he'll be surprised all right," thought the pastor, but thought better of saying this out loud.

But at least he had the unanimous support of the Session to invite the good Doctor, "and if he did accept the invitation maybe he would see fit to suggest my name to a little bit larger church one day soon."

Early the next morning he eagerly sat down at the typewriter to write the fateful and hopeful letter of invitation. I know many of you have never heard of a "typewriter" outside a history book, but the church was certainly not going to waste good money on a computer for the pastor to play with. The church treasurer had made that quite clear from the very first day, adding that so far as he was concerned, the Devil invented the fool thing anyhow. But by now our dear pastor had actually learned to use a typewriter, so he composed the following letter to Dr. Portant.

FIRST PRESBYTERIAN CHURCH OF EUREKA

October 3, 2003

The Reverend Doctor Eim N. Portant, Esq.
Cathedral Presbyterian Church
Metropolis City

My Dear Dr. Portant,

You may not remember me, but I heard you preach at the Metrodome in your fair city several years ago, and had the honor of shaking your hand after the service and introducing myself. Just in case you may have forgotten, I mentioned that I was headed for seminary, and you patted me on the back and said, "good boy."

Well you may be surprised to hear from me again, but the Session of First Presbyterian Church in Eureka, of which I have the honor of being pastor, has requested me to invite you to speak at our Spring Bible conference, the week following Easter next year. If that is not a convenient date, we would be happy for you to choose another time more to your liking.

Ours is a mid-sized [slight exaggeration] congregation, rapidly growing [outright lie]. Though not nearly so large as your fantastic church, still we are regarded as one of the more progressive, yet conservative congregations in the whole state, with a great future in the Kingdom. I feel it would be no exaggeration to say that the Lord is greatly blessing us in many ways, and if you could come to our city and deliver a series of messages, which only you could bring, this would be the instrument God would use to put this church on the map, and insure His continued blessing.

Hopefully, and with kindest personal regards, I remain your friend and admirer.

He read and reread the letter, signed his name with the addition of some quickly made up initials under his name to suggest he had a secretary. With a short but urgent prayer, he mailed it off with high hopes.

There was no response that week, nor the next nor the next after that. But at last a letter came from Dr. Portant, or so he thought before opening it. But rather than a warm personal letter from good Dr. Portant himself, it was a form letter and it was signed by his "executive assistant" Vera Stout. Briefly and curtly the letter informed him that Dr. Portant was a very busy man and the pastor of a dynamic, growing church, and very much in demand as a conference speaker, adjunct professor at the denominational seminary, confidant of presidents and kings and therefore only able to respond to invitations to speak when the following terms were met: 1. A request for his services must be submitted at least two years prior to the desired time. 2. The request must come from a church of at least a thousand members, with no less than five hundred in attendance at each service. 3. Adequate accommodations must be provided at a nearby Hotel, and no meals are to be taken in homes of members, but it would be permissible to invite Dr. Portent to the country club for dinner one evening. 4. All expenses of travel and preparation must be covered and an honorarium appropriate for a man of Dr. Portant's gifts and position will be expected. There were other "rules and regulations" mentioned and a form to fill out indicating a willingness to meet the conditions.

It seemed that a very soggy, wet blanket descended upon the pastor's head as he read the letter. Even ministerial exaggeration stretched to the limit could not make less than a hundred members into a thousand, and as for promising at least five hundred in attendance for each service, well that too was the impossible dream. The letter made it very clear that the hope of having the great Doctor Portant in Eureka had vanished like the morning mist on a hot day. Maybe the homiletics professor from his alma mater, or even the president might agree to come for the hoped-for conference, but that too was highly improbable.

So at the next session meeting a report was made, in a very general way in which the pastor said that Dr. Portant deeply regretted his inability to respond to the gracious invitation due to the heavy demands of his schedule. The pastor expressed regrets that he could not remember Dr. Portant's exact words, and that he had mislaid the letter. So the idea and great hopes of having a prominent preacher for a series of services faded into the oblivion of "maybe we can discuss this at a later time."

Before the meeting ended one of the elders suggested that rather than spending time trying to line up an expensive guest preacher, the pastor would use his time better working on his own sermons, and to stop using so many big words. Another elder thought that maybe we should invite the local Pentecostal preacher in for a series. He had heard that at every service his church was full and the people left church feeling really pumped up. No motion was made, however, and the meeting ended with another, "we'll look into this later."

CHAPTER 7
I SAW THE LIGHT — OR DID I?

Then one magic evening, Dr. Goodbody calls with the exciting news that he may have found just the right place for him to advance in the ministry. The long-awaited, longed-for, prayed-for phone call has finally come. Dr. Goodbody knows of a very promising situation which will soon be open. "This could mean a major step forward in your career if you play your cards just right. This plum of a position is in a major city not too far from denominational headquarters, which definitely sweetens the pot, so to speak."

Dreams do indeed come true, our young pastor thinks. "Please tell me more, Dr. Goodbody."

"An old friend of mine, Dr. Lovingood, is looking for a bright young man like you who could serve as his assistant for the next few years, and perhaps be trained to become his replacement in due time. The church is in a comfortable and stable residential area on the better side of town, and offers so many advantages to a young man on his way up. With its location this church will not have to face some of the problems which occur when a more 'undesirable element' begins to move in. Do you think you might be interested?"

"Of course I am honored, sir, and very, very interested, though it would be difficult to leave my congregation. The Lord is really blessing my work here, and the people do love me so." He fervently hopes Dr. Goodbody does not ask for any details of this assessment.

"Just be patient, and wait to hear from Dr. Lovingood. He will no doubt be in touch soon."

Too excited to concentrate on his work or even sleep very much for a while, our hero finds himself day dreaming about the prospects for significant advancement this could

37

mean in his chosen career. A few days later another phone call of an entirely different nature comes his way. Mrs. Wilson, widow of the former clerk of session, calls and requests a visit as soon as the pastor can work it into his busy schedule. He starts to explain that home visitation is a thing of the past, and besides he really is quite busy, but something in her voice tells him to respond. "Let me see if I can cancel a few things and come out tomorrow afternoon." Somewhat exasperated and more than a little annoyed at the intrusion into his "busy schedule", he nevertheless shows up at Mrs. Wilson's modest little home the next afternoon. He is greeted with a warm and motherly hug, which he finds a little embarrassing, and a hot cup of tea with a few cookies which he doesn't find embarrassing. After a few minutes of chitchat he glances at his watch and mentions his "busy schedule" again.

"Of course, dear, I do understand, but could you spare a lonely old widow a few more minutes? I have a special request to make. You see the doctor told me that I have terminal cancer, and at the most a very few months to live. I need your prayers, and your promise to preach my funeral when I die." Stunned into silence, he suddenly realizes that he really does care very much for this dear lady. Tears rush into his eyes unbidden. Mrs. Wilson reaches over and pats his hand.

"It's all right dear Pastor, I'll be with my beloved Jim again, and with my sweet Lord. Just promise me that you will be there when I need you, and that you will conduct my funeral." He has never witnessed such quiet confidence and true peace in anyone ever before, nor has he ever experienced it for himself.

"I'll be there for you, Mrs. Wilson, just call me any time. It will be a sad honor and privilege to conduct your memorial service when the time comes. But I'm going to pray God will give you relief from pain, and much more time on earth."

"Thank you so much, Pastor. May the Lord's will be done." As the pastor prays, her hand reaches out and takes his and he feels both the tremble of age and illness, and the strength of faith.

As he drives back to his study, he begins to feel an uncomfortable sense of shame, and surprisingly, a reluctance to consider leaving his congregation, but that's just a passing thought, he reassures himself. At least he will fulfill his promise to Mrs. Wilson, and maybe by then he will hear from Dr. Lovingood. Back at the office, his answering machine tells him a message is waiting, and as he listens to the playback he is amazed to hear, "This is Godfrey Lovingood speaking, would you be kind enough to call me at your convenience? Please feel free to call collect. I am most anxious to speak with you as soon as possible."

He stares at the machine for several moments. It's really happening. What seemed like a future possibility, now apparently looms as an immediate prospect for exciting and promising things.

His excitement is overwhelming. He can't wait to tell his wife that their Siberian exile may be drawing to an end. Back to civilization! The future is now, and it is suddenly much brighter than before. He remembers an old line from somewhere in the remote past: "The future is as bright as the promises of God." It is precisely at this point he suddenly comes to the realization that he has not even asked God for His will. In fact with his busy schedule of ministry, he has not really had the time to consult with God about much of anything. Of course his rather lengthy and well-phrased pastoral prayer every Sunday makes up for it . . . or does it? And why in all the world is there a nagging sense of uneasiness in his heart just now? "Get hold of yourself, you're on your way to better things. Return that phone call as soon as you get home and don't make it collect!"

That phone call is going to change a lot of things, but not in the way he expects; oh no, not at all as he expects. Just wait and see.

CHAPTER 8
AN UNEXPECTED ENCOUNTER

"A day is with the Lord as a thousand years, and a thousand years as a day." For our young pastor, only the former is true. He has decided to wait one day before returning the call from Dr. Lovingood lest he seem too eager. The seconds tick slowly by, minutes become hours, the day with no end is upon him. Yet, pass it finally does, and with trembling fingers he dials the magic number which may open the doors of opportunity at last.

After passing through three lower tier levels of secretaries, he arrives at long last in the upper room of the pastor's office, only to be greeted by yet another feminine voice, the pastor's secretary who wants to know who is calling, and why. Too excited to be annoyed, he gives his name, and simply says he is returning a call from Dr. Lovingood, and is unsure of the nature of that call. After a few more rapid-fire questions as to the birthplace of his grandmother, and his social security number, he at last hears the firm, calm, but also gentle voice of Dr. Lovingood. "I'm so glad you returned my call, but you should have called collect. Would it be possible for you to come over here for a visit soon? I'd love to talk with you, get acquainted, and tell you more about our staff position we're trying to fill. Do you have any open dates on your calendar these next few weeks?"

"Well, sir, it just so happens that tomorrow is one of those rare days. Should I bring my wife with me?"

"Perhaps it would be better to do that at a later date," replies Dr. Lovingood.

So arrangements are made, and early the next morning he is off to the city, having slept little, if any, the night before. His wife, though a little hurt that she is not included, accepts

41

the wisdom of patience, and stays behind to pray and wait. And just to make sure, she also crosses her fingers.

After being ushered through the lower echelons of staff, he is at last seated in the presence of the man who represents for him all his hopes and aspirations, as well as occupying the office and positions he hopes will soon be his. Godfrey Lovingood is not at all what he expected of such a prominent man. He is rather short, slightly bald, and seems totally unimpressed with himself. How such a man ever made it so big in the ministry defies explanation.

"Tell me about yourself," he asks, and before long our hero is relaxed and talking like a schoolboy about his childhood, his family, the grief experienced when his father did not come home from Viet Nam. "Neither did my son," responds Dr. Lovingood. Suddenly a bond is forged, and heart begins to speak to heart. "Tell me about your experience with the Lord," probes Dr. Lovingood.

"Well, sir, when I was thirteen, at summer camp," he begins. . .

"No son, I mean now, what's going on between you and the Lord. Tell me about your devotional life, and your leadership in your family life. Talk to me about the last person you led to the Lord." These are the last questions he had expected to hear from this prominent pastor. His answers are not quite honest, in fact they are nowhere near the truth, and Dr. Lovingood seems to sense this, yet in an understanding way. "Tell me why you believe your work for the Lord in your present church is over, and why you believe God may be leading you to this work." Again, questions which had not even entered his mind.

"Sir," he begins, "I'm not sure how to answer your questions," he responds.

"Why not begin by being totally honest with yourself and with me," suggests Dr. Lovingood. "Do you really think God has finished the work through you in your present church? Secondly, do you sense God is calling you to work with me in this church? Far too many of us see the ministry as a career to be pursued like any other career. But it's not just any other career. It is a calling from God, and that means each step, every decision, and most certainly every move from one field to another must not be viewed as a career move, but as a conscious act of obedience to the One who has called us into His service. Oh, I know this sounds idealistic and maybe naive, but unless you truly believe this you have no place in God's service. Please forgive me if I sound judgmental, I only want to spare you some of the pain and heartache I have gone through, and inflicted upon God's flock along the way."

"Yes, you can be successful in the eyes of the world, and unfortunately in the eyes of most of your fellow pastors, but still be a failure as a true servant of God. He has called you to preach Christ and Him crucified, and to qualify for that you must determine that you are crucified with Him, and only live now by and through and for Him."

"My son, lay your ambition before the Lord on the cross. How does it look from there? If you try to do God's work by the world's standards you are either doomed to miserably fail, or even more miserably succeed. Remember both of us, all of us must appear before the judgment seat of Christ to give account of the ministry He has entrusted to us. Forgive me for being so preachy and plain-spoken, but I have a burden for the ministry, and for what's happening in our ranks."

The young pastor sits quietly for a moment, he tries to speak, but cannot think what to say. In his heart, he knows and feels the truth of what he has heard, but even more he senses the love and the true humility of this man who sits before him. Much to his own surprise he hears himself saying, "Dr. Lovingood, right now all I can think of is how much I miss my Dad. That doesn't make much sense, does it?" With that he burst in uncontrolled weeping and thinks to himself, "I've really blown it, what will Dr. Lovingood think of me now?"

Great things are just around the corner. Stay with us to find out.

CHAPTER 9
AN OPEN DOOR — AND HEART

As our young pastor sits in Dr. Lovingood's office, having just lost control of his emotions, he feels an inner turmoil. What the good Doctor has said to him has laid bare all his misconceptions of what the ministry is all about. He is confused, ashamed, and at the same time tremendously impressed by what he has heard. His fears that he has "blown it" by his emotional outburst are groundless. Dr. Lovingood speaks to calm his troubled mind. "Never be ashamed of honest emotions nor of letting them show to a brother who really cares about you. I think this has been building up in you for a long time, but I don't apologize for being the catalyst to bring it all to a head. When you feel like it, let's continue our talk."

"Thank you, sir, for understanding and for all that you just told me. I think for the first time I'm beginning to understand some things I should have grasped long ago. But, frankly, what you have just said goes against the grain of so much I've been told about the ministry. Please tell me what I ought to do."

Dr. Lovingood pauses for a moment, and then continues, "I really can't tell you that. I do not want to get in the way of the Holy Spirit, but I will pray with you and for you that the Lord will give you guidance, and an understanding of His will for your life."

After simple but heartfelt prayers by both men, Dr. Lovingood continues, "Do you want to talk now about our staff position?"

The young pastor's response surprises him more than it does Dr. Lovingood. "With all due respect sir, I really don't think either of us should even consider me for this position. I came here with great eagerness to 'apply' for the opening, thinking this would be a major step up in my 'career,' but with no sense at all of any real leading of the Lord. When you asked me why I thought God might be calling me to this work, I was devastated, not by the question, but because I had never sought His will, or even paused to think about it. What's really strange and embarrassing to admit is that I accepted the call to Eureka Church because it was the only viable opening available and not because I felt any compelling call of the Lord. In fact, I dreaded going there, and was embarrassed because it was so small and out of the way. However, right now I can look you in the eye and tell you that God brought me to Eureka to be the pastor of His people there even though at the time I did not recognize what had happened. Everyone tells me that this is nothing but a maintenance ministry, and that I should leave as soon as possible."

"I'm not sure what your friends and many of my peers mean by 'maintenance' ministry, but what's so bad about maintaining a witness for the Lord in small places, and encouraging the saints, catechizing the children, and comforting the dying? Is this not God's work? You have a great opportunity to make a great deal of difference in a few lives, while people like me can only hope to make a little difference in many lives. Which did our Lord Jesus do when he was on earth?"

"Dr. Lovingood, I'm going back to Eureka. Maybe God will call me to another work one day, or maybe He will keep me there as long as I live. I want you to help me have a better ministry where God has placed me. What should I do, and how can I begin to really minister to the saints, and where do I begin to reach out to find the lost for whom Christ died?"

"I truly believe you are making a wise and godly decision to stay where you are until you know the Lord is calling you to another work. You and I both should have the same attitude that Paul expressed when he called himself a 'slave of Christ.' There is much the Lord can and, I believe, will do through you in Eureka. Let me offer a few suggestions of a general nature, and also assure you of my ongoing availability as a brother and mentor if you want me in those roles."

Let's find out in our next chapter some of the good advice Dr. Lovingood passed on to his younger brother in the Lord.

CHAPTER 10
THE RE-EDUCATION OF A PASTOR

"Dr. Lovingood, there's nothing I would like more than to hear suggestions from you on the ministry the Lord has given me." Our young pastor is more open and teachable than he has ever been before, and more eager to truly minister to his flock.

Dr. Lovingood senses his sincerity and desire to be God's servant and breathes a prayer that the Lord will minister to his young brother through his words of counsel. "Tell me what you are doing now. Describe for me a typical day or week in your schedule. How do you spend your time?"

"Well, sir, I try to work hard, but I don't always feel that I accomplish much. I try to be at the study by 9:00 a.m., and leave strict orders not to be interrupted before lunch. I'm back from lunch by 1:00 or 1:30 and keep at my work till late afternoon unless there's an emergency of some kind, and then I make my rounds at the local hospital between 4:00 and 5:00 if there is anyone sick. Once a month I go by the nursing home to see the five retirees we have there. Sometimes one of the flock may come by the study, but I require an appointment to be made first to maximize my time. Of course there are officer meetings in the evenings, a few committees, the men's club, the women's organization, and the youth activities, such as they are."

"My friend it is obvious to me that you work harder than many men I know in the ministry, but let's take a closer look. What is it that you spend so much time doing in your study?"

"Well, I have the usual Sunday sermon to prepare, plus once a month we have an evening service, but that's usually more of a hymn-sing than anything. Then, there is the men's Sunday school class, and the Wednesday Bible study. Of course I try to keep up my reading in theology and in many other areas as well. I try to make copies of all my sermons and lessons and distribute them to the congregation or class ahead of time. I spend a good deal of time with my computer (It's just a typewriter, but he calls it a computer.) cranking out schedules, lesson plans, and well, a lot of other things. That takes a lot of time, too."

"How much time do you spend just being with your people and seeing them in their homes? Do you take time to see your men at their business or shops, or maybe for lunch?"

"No sir, I just can't seem to find the time, and besides, we were told at seminary that social visiting in the homes is a waste of time."

"If all you were doing was making a 'social call' I might agree, but what I'm talking about are pastoral calls on your people to get to know them and to encourage and comfort them. You might be surprised how many of your people have deep needs and heartaches, how few of them have any real assurance of salvation. The sheep need a shepherd to do more than deliver well-thought-out theological discourses. Not that hard study isn't important, it is. But you need to strive for more balance."

"I think I'm getting ahead of myself though, so let me go back to your workday. In the first place 9:00 a.m. is too late to begin your day. Yes, take time with your family at breakfast and morning prayers, but even so, you need to be in your study earlier. You said you left strict orders not to be interrupted before noon. That can be good and bad. You should begin each workday with an appointment." The young man looks puzzled, but Dr. Lovingood goes on, "not with men, but with the Lord. Make that first hour a serious appointment with God in prayer and in personal feeding upon the Word. I don't mean as study time for a sermon or lesson, but for your own soul's good. You mentioned that four of your Elders and two Deacons were retired. Why not ask them to come to your study once a week right after your own devotional time. Serve them coffee and ask them to pray with you. It may take a while, but some will respond, and you will be building a bond with them as nothing else could possibly do."

"Learn to use your study time more productively. Do your people really need all those many pages of notes and sermons . . . all of them ? What do you suppose they do with them? It is so easy for the sacred duty of study to become a sinful excuse for neglecting your flock in other ways. Take at least three afternoons and two evenings each week to go into the homes of your people, and when possible take your wife with you. She needs that sense of sharing in your ministry and of feeling a part of your work. Besides," he smiles, "they might rather see her than you at times. You told me many of your people are elderly and retired. These you may see in the afternoons. Arrange for your home visits in the evenings when the whole family is present. Let them know you really care for them. They will open up to you before long. You can guide them into a close personal relationship to the Lord. Many older people tend to develop fears and anxieties which may rob them of assurance and peace. You can be used of the Good Shepherd to help 'restore their souls.'"

"Use your home as a ministry base, as well. Invite families in to share your Sunday dinner, or for times of fellowship during the week. Try to get the children in your congregation to come by your study one afternoon each week. Get your wife to help you, and have something good to snack on, and then begin to teach them the catechism. Then encourage the dads and moms to continue this study at home. Your leadership is so important in these things. While you're at it, teach them to pray, too. If they know you are interested in them and will take some time with them, they will be your best friends and most avid supporters."

"Finally, dear brother, let me encourage you to preach from your heart to their hearts, as well as mind to mind. Think of each sermon as the last one you may ever preach or that they may ever hear, because both are possibilities. Preach like Jesus preached, in simple language, with easy-to-understand stories like he told that will open both mind and heart to the great truths of God's Word. He never bored people to death, he preached and loved them to life. 'Go thou and do likewise,' and may the Lord's grace rest upon your ministry."

The young pastor leaves with a sense of having heard the voice of the Lord speaking through Dr. Lovingood. Somehow he has forgotten the short stature and balding head. He has been in the presence of a giant, but a sweet and humble giant, who exemplifies all a man of God should be. He finds himself praying and repenting all the way home on the long drive. He feels a Presence far more awesome and far more loving than the good Pastor Lovingood.

But the drive back home is long and lonely. The young pastor is thoughtful and reflective. There were a thousand and one questions he should have asked Dr. Lovingood, but he couldn't think of even one as he listened to the words of wisdom and grace. Now he tries to remember every word, and think through every idea he had heard. "If only Dr. Lovingood was in the car right now, we could talk again." But as he drives along he begins to talk, but not to the good Doctor. "Lord, please forgive me for being such a poor shepherd to Your sheep, and help me to follow You, the good Shepherd, in all my ways. 'Search me and try me, O God, and see if there be any wicked way within me, and lead me in the way everlasting.'" So he prays and talks with the Lord all the way back to Eureka, and for the most of the hours in the days which follow. God works great grace and change in his heart and mind.

Upon arriving home, he takes his wife in his arms and begins to open his heart to her in a way he has never done before. For her, the momentary sting of hearing they won't be leaving Eureka for a while is softened by the realization something real and wonderful has happened to her husband, and she feels closer to him than she has ever felt before and so she also feels closer to the Lord.

CHAPTER 11
TWO WOUNDED WARRIORS ARE HEALED

On Saturday evening, when the pastor is walking to his study for those last few hours of preparation and prayer, his eyes fall on the Church sign, and especially his name, THE REVEREND _____ SENIOR PASTOR. He stops and looks around and then quietly removes THE REVEREND, AND SENIOR, leaving only his name, and the word pastor. Somehow his Saturday evening quiet time and prayer is richer and dearer than ever before, and his sleep is the sleep of the blest.

Early Sunday morning he is back in his study to pray over his sermon notes before the congregation begins to gather. He glances out the window and sees the old man they all call "Captain John" heading into the Church. He inwardly groans, but manages a gracious smile and warm handshake in response to old John's knock. "I seen somebody's been a'messing with your sign out front, Preacher, but I sort of liked it, and thought since you wuzn't a SENIOR Pastor no more, it would be O.K. if I wuz to come in here and pray with you, that is if you don't mind. I'm surely in need of a heap of prayer, and I 'spect maybe you could use some your ownself. Besides I want to show you a little somethin'. It's why they call me 'Captain John.'"

"Captain John, you have no idea how glad I am to see you and pray with you; it is so good of you to come down and pray with me. I apologize for not being available to pray with you sooner."

"You mean that, preacher? Why nobody ever has time for me. They know I'm not quite right in the head, but I ain't always been thisaway."

"John, let's pray first and then you show me what you brought and tell me anything that's on your heart."

So they kneel together, and for the second time (remember Widow Wilson) the pastor really prays with one of his flock. The simple halting prayer of Old John touches his heart, especially when he thanks the Lord for sending such a wonderful pastor. There are mutual tears, and a spontaneous embrace afterwards. "Preacher, maybe you don't have time for old John to show you this little box or tell you how I come by it."

A glance at his watch tells the pastor he has a half hour before Sunday School. "Show me, John, and tell me all about it. The box is opened, and before his amazed eyes there is that most coveted prize any soldier may ever win. Not even his heroic father won this prize when he died for his country in Viet Nam.

It is the Congressional Medal of Honor, with a copy of the citation bearing the name of Captain John Sanders. "Why, John, this is really amazing! Please tell me about it."

"Well, preacher, it's like I said, I wuzn't always off in the head. That happened after the last wound I got over in France on June the 6th, 1944. I wuz a sure 'nuff Captain in the U. S. Army, and led a bunch of men onto the beachhead at Omaha beach." The tragic tale of heroism and gallantry unfolds in halting words as old John recalls the horror of that long ago day. The appalling loss of life, the sweeping machine-gun fire, the bursting mortar shells and the pain of the memory is overwhelming as old John sobs out the last few words, "wuzn't no hero then or now, preacher, but I couldn't let them boys just drown and die back there, I had to try. I guess maybe I dragged eight or ten to the wall before that first bullet found me. But it took three more and a big old hunk of shrapnel to put me down to stay. I guess some fellers saw what I done and told the C.O. about it. Anyway when I finally come to my senses over in England and could walk a little they done give me this one day and said I wuz a hero. Just thought maybe you'd like to know. Nobody else seems to care anymore. Don't reckon many folks remember or ever even heard about it at all."

"John, you have paid me an honor as precious to me as your medal is to you. I am ashamed I haven't seemed to care about you before, please forgive me, and would you meet me here each Sunday for prayer? And, yes, Captain, you are a real hero to me."

Alone again for a few minutes before the congregation begins to come in, the pastor is again on his knees, praying for brave Captain Sanders, wounded Captain Sanders, lonely old John, and many others in the congregation as well. As he walks into the pulpit after Sunday school, there is a feeling that he is walking into that sacred place for the first time as the true pastor of his flock, though the sermon that follows is not quite the one he had prepared.

Chapter 12
All Is Well That Never Ends

As the congregation slowly assembles for worship, (beginning, of course, with the back seats), the pastor, often in the past impatient to get the "preliminaries" over so the important part of the service, his well-prepared theological lecture, might begin, senses that he, and his congregation are truly standing on Holy Ground. He will soon begin the service of worship in these words, "In the name of the Father, the Son, and the Holy Spirit." How awesome is this place, where people might come together in that holy and majestic name, and claim His presence and blessing. A joy mingled with wonder-struck humility fills his heart and soul. The prelude is over, silence begins to fall upon the congregation, except of course for Widow Jenkins, who is so near deaf she doesn't know the organ has ceased, nor does she realize her stage whisper is really several decibels above a good country shout. But even she can see the pastor walk to the pulpit, so quietness prevails, as he begins his call to worship in a slightly different manner than before.

"Brothers and Sister, beloved of Christ, we have met here for worship in the name and for the glory of our great God and Savior. Let us stand in His presence and contemplate His greatness and goodness in a few moments of silent prayer and adoration." Although a little confused by a slight difference in the usual call to worship, yet aware that a new note of tenderness and reverence is detected in their pastor's voice, they respond, and many even truly pray.

As the service continues, there is an undeniable enthusiasm and sincerity in the pastor's words, his singing, and even in his facial expression that is contagious, and begins to affect all the worshipers. Some are a little uncomfortable, but most respond appreciatively to what is happening. "God Himself is with us," sings the choir and from many hearts there is a silent amen (This is still a Presbyterian church!).

The Scripture is read from Romans, chapter eight, and then a brief prayer for illumination follows. Not the usual formal and well-turned phrases heard so often before, but a gentle pleading for the Spirit's presence and power upon His word and His people. "Dear people, I am about to preach to you the first real sermon you have ever heard me preach. Oh yes, I've been in the pulpit for well over a year now and have spoken many times, but as I have reflected upon this past year, what I have really done is deliver a series of well-prepared, carefully documented, and theologically correct lectures. I have not preached the Word of God to your hearts with the conviction that by His word, God will work grace and holiness in your lives. Even this morning's message as announced in the bulletin attests to what I am saying. You will notice the sermon title is "*Ordo Salutis*" whatever that may mean to you. I was prepared, with full manuscript, and a detailed, seven-page outline for you to follow, which you have noticed was not in your hymn-book racks this morning. They were there last night, but I took them up this morning, because I want you just to listen with your hearts and hear the Holy Spirit speaking through His word. I assure you that everything in my manuscript is true to the best of my ability to understand truth, but the way I prepared this message, it would have little application to your lives. So bear with me while I try, by the Holy Spirit's illumining power to tell you how our great God saves sinners, and keeps them in His precious love for all eternity."

There follows a simple but profound exposition of that great passage from Romans which thrills the heart, challenges the mind, comforts the saint, and calls the sinner to repentance. The sermon is just as theologically correct as ever, but so much more alive and powerful than has been heard in many a day in Eureka. The mystery of sovereign grace and electing mercy is presented winsomely with illustrations from Scripture and from life to demonstrate the meaning and application. The mighty Holy Spirit works in the lives of the people. No one thinks about the time, or that the Baptist and Methodist may beat them to the cafeteria after church. The last chorus of the closing hymn is sung with conviction and gratitude, "On Christ, the solid rock I stand, all other ground is sinking sand." And because it is sung by people who have heard the word of God in faith and with joy, the sound of that singing is heard in heaven, and their faith is counted to them as righteousness, and the glorious God who has been worshiped in spirit and in truth receives this worship and is well pleased.

The benediction falls upon that congregation as a gentle shower of rain after a long drought, and the raindrops of that blessing are mingled with tears in many eyes, as the reality of grace, mercy and peace is experienced. There is no rushing to leave this Sunday; but a lingering, a reluctance to leave that blessed place, where God has met with his people. A beginning has been made, a true work of grace has begun, and the story of the great revival that falls upon that little congregation and that little out-of-the-way town will be talked about with wonder and awe for generations to come, and in many places. Dr. Lovingood finds another man for his assistant, and alas, our beloved young pastor is never invited back to speak to the students at his alma mater.